Table of Contents

i

MP3418

Table of Contents

MP341

Name _____   Date _____

Q as a Beginning Sound

Practice writing **qu** on the line. Color all the pictures that begin with **qu**.

_____

- -

_____

  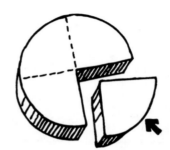 

1

MP3418

Name _____ Date _____

X as a Final Sound

Write the letter or letters for the final sound you hear in each word.

so _____ si _____ du _____ fo _____

bo _____ ja _____ a _____ ki _____

o _____ en e _____ it si _____ ty ne _____

MP341

Name _____ Date _____

Hard and Soft C Sounds

Circle the sound you hear in each word.

s k	s k	s k	s k	s k
s k	s k	s k	s k	s k
s k	s k	s k	s k	s k
s k	s k	s k	s k	s k

MP3418

Name _____   Date _____

Hard and Soft C Sounds

Underline words in the paragraphs containing the letter C that sound like /s/.
Circle the words containing the letter C that sound like /k/.

Meaghan and Courtney could climb on the monkey bars during recess, but they could not play on them now because they were just painted. They joined the boys playing soccer. The ball bounced over Courtney's head and went out of bounds. Curt threw it in to Carl who caught it. He carefully passed it toward the fence where Nancy carried it down the field and made a goal. The ball was brought to the center line and put down in the circle. Play continued until one o'clock when the bell clanged. It was time for science.

The cages for the guinea pigs and mice blocked the first entrance to the science lab, so the class went to the second door. They took encyclopedias off the shelf and began working on their research papers. Then the instructor said, "Close your books. Face me, keep your voices down, and watch while I place this test tube over the fire." The heat turned the clear fluid in the tube cerise. He asked the center section to tell what caused the reaction. They decided the heat made the particles of the fluid collide, and that is what changed the color. Then the teacher instructed the class to record the experiment on an index card and to place it in the file cabinet.

MP3418

Hard and Soft SC Sounds

Complete the sentences below using words from the word box.

science	seen	sent	sense	cent	scene	scissors
scents	scenery	scenic	sciatic	scent	cents	scented
						scissor

1. The boys were _____ at the movies.

2. The second act, _____ three, is scheduled for 8:00.

3. All he had in his pocket was a rubber band and one _____.

4. Get out the paste and _____ for this activity.

5. The stage crew painted all the background _____.

6. When you swim the side stroke, you are supposed to do the _____ kick with your legs.

7. When our neighbors opened their front door, wonderful _____ floated out to greet us.

8. The skunk gave us a warning not to come closer by giving up a terrible _____.

9. The _____ teacher had us work on chemical experiments.

10. We followed the _____ route when we drove in the mountains.

There are three different groups of homonyms in the box. What are they?

_____

_____

_____

MP3418

Hard and Soft G Sounds

Circle the sound you hear in each word.

g j	g j	g j	g j	g j
g j	g j	g j	g j	g j
g j	g j	g j	g j	g j
g j	g j	g j	g j	g j

MP3418

Hard and Soft G Sounds

Draw a line under the words in each sentence that have the same G sound. Write G after the sentence if the sound is /g/. Write J after the sentence if the sound is /j/.

1. A great crowd gathered on the village green. _____

2. The gentle giant hugged the children. _____

3. The judge pounded his gavel for the group to be seated. _____

4. After their marriage, the bride and groom rode in a carriage to the lodge. _____

5. The hinge on the cage fell to the ground. _____

6. The green garden grew under the bridge. _____

7. A huge gorilla growled at the onlookers against the fence. _____

8. Mary put her goldfish in a golden glass. _____

9. A large page fell from the kindergarten book. _____

10. The jolly giant enjoyed juggling grapefruits. _____

11. Goldfish and guppies sometimes live together. _____

12. We played bingo and George won the game. _____

13. Goblins and ghosts are on the move on Halloween. _____

14. My guest was going to dust her room with a rag. _____

15. Glass scattered everywhere when Georgia dropped the goblet. _____

16. In geology we studied about gems and gold. _____

17. The orange fish swam under the bridge. _____

18. The huge engine gently pulled the train. _____

19. The gentleman raised the gate on the bridge to let the barge through. _____

20. The gopher and gorilla were in cages at the zoo. _____

MP3418

Name _____ Date _____

Review Q, X, Hard/Soft C and G

Write the letter or letters for the sound you hear in each word.

___ iant	___ ___ ill	___ eneral	___ ity	___ ypsy
66 si ___ ty- si ___	dan ___ er	___ orilla	___ ara ___ e	___ ems
offi ___ er	o ___ en	e ___ ___ al	___ ir ___ le	en ___ ine
___ iraffe	gro ___ ery ___ art	___ arba ___ e	___ alf	li ___ ___ id

MP3418

Recognizing Different Sounds of C, G, K, S, J

The words below have one letter underlined. Write each word under the correct heading.

Example: mon<u>k</u>ey   The underlined letter K says /k/, so it goes in the K says /k/ column.

<u>g</u>uest	ea<u>s</u>y	<u>g</u>entle	han<u>k</u>y	<u>c</u>rystal	that'<u>s</u>
i<u>c</u>e cream	<u>g</u>eography	que<u>s</u>tion	<u>j</u>ockey	<u>g</u>oblet	banda<u>g</u>e
ca<u>s</u>tle	<u>S</u>usie	spi<u>k</u>ed	gara<u>g</u>e	<u>g</u>loves	ban<u>j</u>o
exer<u>c</u>ise	ma<u>j</u>or	<u>c</u>ellar	ti<u>g</u>er	wi<u>s</u>e	<u>c</u>ertificate
po<u>k</u>er	race<u>s</u>	<u>k</u>ettle	ex<u>c</u>use	li<u>s</u>ten	se<u>c</u>ret
cou<u>s</u>in	<u>c</u>alcium	<u>c</u>yclone	cu<u>c</u>umber	ma<u>j</u>ority	

S says /s/	C says /s/	K says /k/	C says /k/
_____	_____	_____	_____
_____	_____	_____	_____
_____	_____	_____	_____
_____	_____	_____	_____

J says /j/	G says /j/	G says /g/	S says /z/
_____	_____	_____	_____
_____	_____	_____	_____
_____	_____	_____	_____

MP3418

Sounds of /n/

N says /n/ in the following ways: <u>kn</u>ow   <u>gn</u>aw   <u>n</u>ever

Write **kn**, **gn**, or **n** in the blanks to complete the words below.

_____ ife	_____ eedle	_____ apsack	_____ at
_____ ee	_____ ocker	_____ ewspaper	_____ ickers
_____ ickel	_____ ome	_____ uckles	_____ ob
_____ itting	_____ ecklace	_____ ot	_____ u

MP3418

Name _____   Date _____

Sounds of the Spelling GH

When the letters **gh** come together in a word, they are usually silent or make the sound /f/.

Examples: **right**—gh is silent. (rīt)

  laugh—gh says /f/. (laf)

Read the story below. Mark an X on any **gh** that is silent. Circle any **gh** that makes the sound /f/.

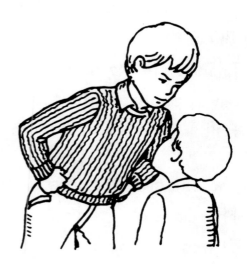

Billy was the tough kid in our class, or at least he thought he was. He weighed more than anyone else, and he was taller, too. Billy was strong and liked to pick fights. First he would laugh at someone smaller. If that did not make them want to fight, he would push them through a door. One night Billy laughed at Troy. That was the wrong person for Billy to bother. Troy did not care that Billy stood taller than he. Troy caught Billy by his thigh. They fought. Troy taught Billy a lesson. Now Billy uses his height and weight to help people lift and move heavy objects and reach things high up instead of using them to beat up on people smaller than he is.

Several words below contain the letters **gh**. Write the words with a silent **gh** on line 1. Write the words with the /f/ sound in a sentence on line 2.

though   bought   cough   rough   ought   dough   ghost   trough

1. _____

2. _____

One word is different from the others. Which one is it, and how is it different?

_____

_____

MP3418

Sounds of /f/

Underline all the letters in the words below that make the /f/ sound.

1. The dolphins were favorites at the zoo.
2. The football players autographed my scrapbook.
3. The hunters shot three pheasants and five ducks.
4. Phonics are the sounds of the alphabet's letters.
5. An elephant's skin is tough.
6. Father fixed the hole by the fence so the gopher would stay away from his flowers.
7. The school won a trophy for physical fitness.
8. Physicians are medical doctors.
9. It was a triumphant victory for the fifth grade.
10. No one knew who the phantom visitor was who came every Friday.
11. Everyone laughed at the frisky puppies rolling over each other.
12. Father drove the van over the rough road.
13. A sphere is round like a ball.
14. Our soccer team played the boys from the orphanage.
15. The pigs shared their trough with other farm animals.
16. A phrase is often written by mistake instead of a sentence.
17. The orphan needed physical attention for his cough.
18. Five students failed physics.
19. The audience laughed when the film was on backwards.
20. The graph showed there were fifty more farmers in Iowa than Ohio.
21. Samuel Morse invented the telegraph.
22. The photographer took too many pictures.
23. Physical education is most students' favorite subject.

What letter or letters can make the /f/ sound? _____

MP3418

Name _____ Date _____

/f/ Crossword

Complete the crossword puzzle. Every answer will have the /f/ sound. On the line after each clue, write the letters in the answer that make the /f/ sound.

Across

1. Growth on a tree _____
4. Flat water vehicle _____
8. Expel air from lungs _____
9. Pig's dish _____
11. Response to a joke _____
12. Opposite of smooth _____
13. An African giant _____
15. Not before _____
16. A chart _____

Down

2. One of five on a hand _____
3. Amount that satisfies _____
5. Just terrible _____
6. Instrument for talking _____
7. One without parents _____
10. Heats a house _____
14. Group of two or more related words _____

MP3418

Sounds of S

The letter S can make three different sounds:

/z/ as in race<u>s</u>   /sh/ as in <u>s</u>ure   /zh/ as in mea<u>s</u>ure

Complete the puzzles below. Write in the words for the word box that match the S sound shown.

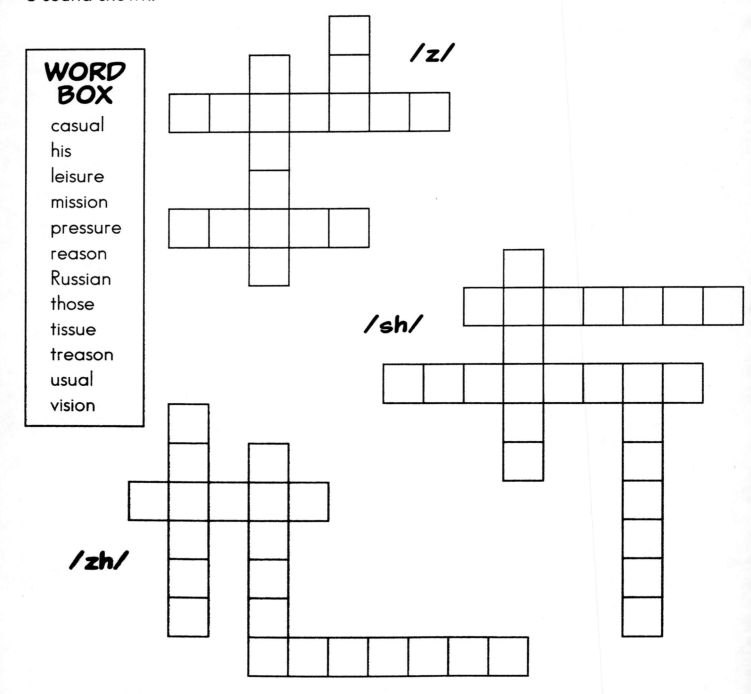

WORD BOX

casual
his
leisure
mission
pressure
reason
Russian
those
tissue
treason
usual
vision

/z/

/sh/

/zh/

14

Sounds of Spelling CH

CH is a digraph. It can make three different sounds:

/ch/ as in mu<u>ch</u>   /k/ as in a<u>ch</u>e   /sh/ as in <u>ch</u>ute

Complete the crossword puzzles below. Use words from the word box that fit the definition and sound shown.

WORD BOX

chain	orchid
orchestra	chop
charades	ache
ranch	machine
parachute	church
champagne	chef

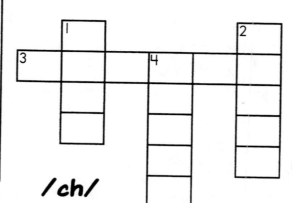

/ch/

/k/

/sh/

Across
3. A place of worship

Down
1. A cut of meat
2. Connected metal links
4. Where cattle are raised

Across
3. Instruments playing together

Down
1. A flower
2. Throbbing hurt

Across
1. Bubbly drink with which to make a toast
4. Man-made contraption

Down
1. Game in which a word or phrase is acted out
2. Used to jump from plane
3. Person who cooks.

MP3418

Sounds of Spelling SH

The /sh/ sound is made by several letter combinations. Read the story below. Circle words with the /sh/ sound, as head in **sheep**.

The ambitious scientist was working on a theory he thought might make an impression on the world. His actions in the laboratory caused the machines to shake vigorously. He had to turn his attention from his invention to the machinery. His quick action corrected the problem without much distraction from his project.

It was essential that the scientist give injections to his precious mouse, Charlotte. She did not like being shot with a needle and made an impression on the scientist's hand with her sharp teeth. He went to a doctor, who assured him his hand would be alright, but the doctor gave him some antibiotics for insurance.

The scientist had some hesitation about finishing the experiments, but he was tenacious and put on special gloves, thin as tissue paper, for protection. His facial expression was stern as he set out to do the next section with determination.

Write the letter combinations that make the /sh/ sound in the boxes below. Then write the words with the matching letter combinations under the appropriate headings.

MP3418

Name _____ Date _____

T Followed By U Sound

Choose a word from the word box that fits each definition below. Write the circled letters in order on the blanks at the bottom of the page. They will tell about a sound heard in all these words.

fracture	mutual	pasture	creature	picture
furniture	moisture	dentures	departure	actually
factually	situation	sanctuaries		

A wall hanging __ __ __ ◯ __ __

Time of leaving __ __ __ ◯ __ __ __ __ __

A broken bone ◯ __ __ __ ◯ __ __ __

Weird-looking beast __ __ ◯ __ __ __ ◯ __

Where cattle graze __ __ __ ◯ __ __ __

Chairs, tables, beds, sofa __ __ ◯ __ __ __ __ __ __

Humidity __ ◯ __ __ ◯ __ __ __

A condition __ __ __ ◯ __ __ __ __

Something in common __ __ __ __ __ ◯ __

Really exists __ __ __ __ ◯ __ ◯ __ __

Set of teeth __ __ __ __ __ __ ◯ __

Truly __ __ __ ◯ __ __ ◯ __

Places of refuge ◯ __ __ __ __ __ __ __ __ __

__ __ __ __ __ __ __ __ __ __ __ __ __

__ __ __ __ /ch/ as in **vulture.**

MP3418

Recognizing Silent Letters

Name _____   Date _____

Read the name of each picture. Draw a line through each silent letter in the word.

lamb	knot	wrist	comb
sign	chalk	wren	light
calf	thumb	ghost	fight
gnat	knob	crumbs	half

MP341

Rhyming Silent Letter Words

The words in each row have the same silent letters. Write the name of each picture and draw a line through the silent letters. Some words have extra silent letters.

__knight__ _____ _____ _____

__wrestle__ _____ _____ _____

__knit__ _____ _____ _____

 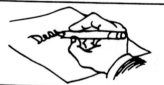  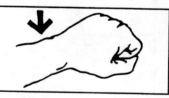

__wren__ _____ _____ _____

   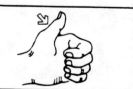

__bomb__ _____ _____ _____

MP3418

Spelling Silent Letter Words

Write the silent letters missing in the words below. Some are consonants, and some are vowels.

ha ___ f	b ___ ilding	crum ___ s	tong ___ ___
cas ___ l ___	s ___ ord	si ___ n	glas ___ ___
ya ___ ___ t	___ ni ___ ___ t	s ___ is ___ ors	___ re ___ th
slei ___ ___	___ res ___ ler	cra ___ k	___ nom ___

20

MP3418

Name _____ Date _____

Cross Out Silent Letters

Some consonants in words have no sound—they are silent. Sometimes vowels are silent, too. Read the following statements, and then follow the directions.

W is silent before **r** at the beginning of a word. Draw a line through the silent letters in each word below.

wring	wrangler	wrench	wrinkle	wrap
wrestle	wrung	wrong	written	wreath

G and **gh** are often silent after the long **a** and long **i** sounds. Draw a line through the silent letters in each word below.

frighten	sign	height	slight	high
weight	delight	bright	weigh	straight

T is silent before **ch** at the end of a word. Draw a line through the silent letters in each word below.

match	crutch	stitch	witch	latch
hutch	twitch	patch	ditch	switch

D is silent before **ge** at the end of a word. Draw a line through the silent letters in each word below.

judge	lodge	trudge	ledge	smudge
pledge	hedge	dodge	grudge	edge

Two-consonant combinations that may be thought of as having a silent letter are double consonants, as in **miss** or **ball**, and the consonant digraph **ck**, as in **buck**. In double consonants at the end of a word, the first letter is heard. In **ck**, the **c** is silent. Draw a line through the silent letters in each word below.

neck	grass	cuff	duck	hall	egg
mitt	kick	lock	jacks	glass	deck

MP3418

Circle Silent Letters

Circle the silent letter or letters in each word below.

flight	comb	guest
listen	hours	wrong
half	sign	bread
thumb	hasten	gnome
climb	stalk	receipt
talk	knave	castle
ditch	crawl	lamb
paint	whistle	corps
chalk	science	sleigh
yacht	sword	answer
bridge	kneel	wrist
biscuit	bright	wrap
wring	psalm	batch
glisten	calm	calf
campaign	coat	bomb
wrestle	cliff	grow
friend	might	write
crayon	moisten	gnaw
antique	knew	two
numb	wren	eight

MP3418

Name _____ Date _____

Writing Diacritical Words

Use the diacritical markings in the box to write the dictionary spellings for the words below.

PRONUNCIATION KEY

a cap	ā cape	ä cart	au flaw	e met	ē meat
i(ə)r ear	a(ə)r air	ər her, bird, turn		ə one	
i pin	ī pine	o got	ō goat	ou out	oi boy
ô or	o͞o pool	o͝o foot	u cut	ū cute	
hw when	ng sing	th thin	th this		

rain _____

scarf _____

king _____

hinge _____

their _____

chalk _____

peace _____

quilt _____

wrench _____

scissor _____

warm _____

ruin _____

choose _____

cart _____

laugh _____

raft _____

judge _____

fern _____

half _____

died _____

witch _____

friend _____

march _____

shelf _____

quiz _____

learn _____

stack _____

chord _____

think _____

kite _____

watch _____

charm _____

heart _____

rescue _____

lamb _____

quiet _____

world _____

shank _____

lion _____

MP3418

Writing Words from Diacritical Markings

Use the diacritical markings in the box to help you write the traditional spellings of the words below.

PRONUNCIATION KEY

a cap	ā cape	ä cart	au flaw	e met	ē meat
i(ə)r ear	a(ə)r air	ər her, bird, turn		ə one	
i pin	ī pine	o got	ō goat	ou out	oi boy
ô or	o͞o pool	o͝o foot	u cut	ū cute	
hw when	ng sing	th thin	<u>th</u> this		

krab _____   smel _____   boks _____

jim _____   auers _____   bābē _____

gōl _____   sēt _____   nōm _____

fōn _____   clīm _____   shef _____

fit _____   kauf _____   ren _____

nob _____   stauk _____   num _____

kwik _____   ej _____   pom _____

ruf _____   kraul _____   grō _____

pāst _____   kuf _____   plēz _____

fa(ə)rē _____   fens _____   akshən _____

sīn _____   luv _____   sho͞or _____

kwīt _____   mēn _____   ho͞o _____

lift _____   ment _____   krust _____

Name _____ Date _____

Answering Diacritical Questions

Read the paragraph below. Then use the pronunciation key to help you figure out and answer the questions. Notice the ə. It is called the "schwa." It is used when none of the other vowel sounds are heard in the word or word part. It makes the sound heard in **one** (wen) or **action** (akshun). Use regular spellings for your answers.

PRONUNCIATION KEY

a cap	ā cape	ä cart	au flaw	e met	ē meat
i(ə)r ear	a(ə)r air	ər her, bird, turn		ə one	
i pin	ī pine	o got	ō goat	ou out	oi boy
ô or	o͞o pool	o͝o foot	u cut	ū cute	
hw when	ng sing	th thin	<u>th</u> this		

The Pilgrims sailed on the Mayflower from Plymouth, England, in September of 1620. They left England because they wanted to practice their religion as they believed, and not as the Church of England wanted them to practice. Their original destination in America was Virginia, but they landed in what is now Massachusetts in December of that same year. The Pilgrims named the new colony in which they settled after the place from which they came—Plymouth. Only half of the 103 passengers survived the first harsh winter in America.

1. Ho͞o iz <u>th</u>ə pa(e)rəgraf əbout? _____

2. Hwī did <u>th</u>ā cum to͞o əma(ə)rəkə? _____

3. Hwen did <u>th</u>ā lēv Ēnglənd? _____

_____

4. How laung did it tāk <u>th</u>em to͞o māk <u>th</u>ə trip? _____

5. Hou menē pasənjərz wər aun <u>th</u>ə Māflouər? _____

MP3418

Reading a Diacritical Story

Many words in the paragraph below are written using dictionary (diacritical) markings. Rewrite the paragraphs using regular spelling patterns. Use the pronunciation key and a dictionary to help you spell correctly. No letters are capitalized. You must determine which letter to capitalize.

PRONUNCIATION KEY

a cap	ā cape	ä cart	au flaw	e met	ē meat
i(ə)r ear	a(ə)r air	ər her, bird, turn		ə one	
i pin	ī pine	o got	ō goat	ou out	oi boy
ô or	o͞o pool	o͝o foot	u cut	ū cute	
hw when	ng sing	th thin	t͟h this		

t͟he modərn ōlympək gāmz wər fərst held in athənz, grēs, in 1896. wən uv t͟he mān gōlz uv t͟he gāmz wuz to͞o prəmōt betər internashunəl undərstanding and coopərāshun thro͞o ə ūnəvərsəl mēdēəm—athletiks.

t͟he ānshənt grēk ōlympək gāmz had much t͟he sām in mīnd hwen t͟hā bēgan ōvər twentē-seven hundrəd yi(ə)rz əgō. nou ōvər wən hundrəd nāshənz cəmpēt in t͟he sumər and wintər gāmz.

_____

_____

_____

_____

_____

_____

_____

_____

MP341

Name _____   Date _____

Writing a Diacritical Story

Rewrite the paragraph below using dictionary (diacritical) markings. Use the pronunciation key to help you. Numbers should be left as they are in the translation. All letters should be lowercase. Make sure to put in punctuation marks.

PRONUNCIATION KEY

a cap	ā cape	ä cart	au flaw	e met	ē meat
i(ə)r ear	a(ə)r air	ər her, bird, turn		ə one	
i pin	ī pine	o got	ō goat	ou out	oi boy
ô or	o͞o pool	o͝o foot	u cut	ū cute	
hw when	ng sing	th thin	th̲ this		

The Statue of Liberty has stood as a symbol of freedom in New York's harbor since 1886. It was given to America by the French government as a symbol of friendship between the two countries. The great lady welcomed millions of immigrants to the new country when the ships on which they were arriving sailed past her on their way to Ellis Island. Not as many immigrants pass the statue today because the newcomers arrive by plane.

_____

_____

_____

_____

_____

_____

_____

MP3418

Double Consonant Endings

Write the final two letters of each word.

cu ___ ___	dre ___ ___	e ___ ___	pa ___ ___
hi ___ ___	mi ___ ___	do ___ ___	ba ___ ___
gla ___ ___	mu ___ ___	dri ___ ___	bu ___ ___
bu ___ ___	gu ___ ___	ki ___ ___	gra ___ ___

28

MP3411

Name _____ Date _____

Initial Sound of Blend DR

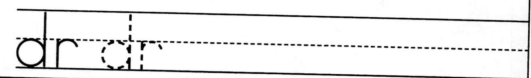

Practice writing dr on the line. Then color the pictures that begin with dr.

dr dr

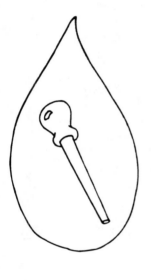 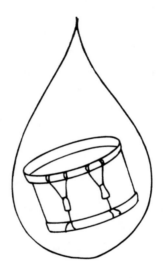 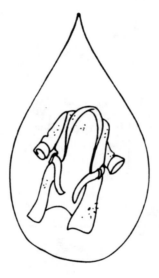 

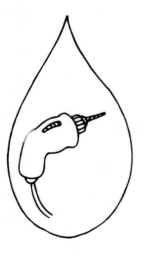   

29

Initial Sound of Blend TR

Practice writing tr on the line. Then color the pictures that begin with tr.

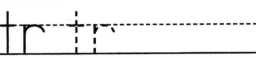

tr tr

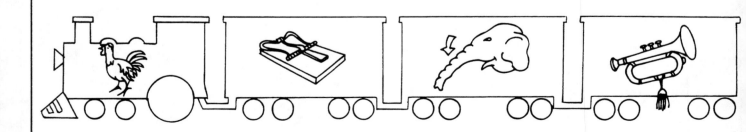

MP341

Name _____ Date _____

Initial Sound of Blends BL, BR

Practice writing **bl** and **br** on the lines. Then write **bl** or **br** to show how the name of each picture begins.

MP3418

Initial Sound of Blends CL, CR

Practice writing cl and cr on the lines. Then write cl or cr to show how the name of each picture begins.

cl

cr

MP341

Name ______________________________ Date ______________

Review QU, DR, TR, BL, BR, CL, CR

Circle the blend that begins the name of each picture below. The first one is done for you.

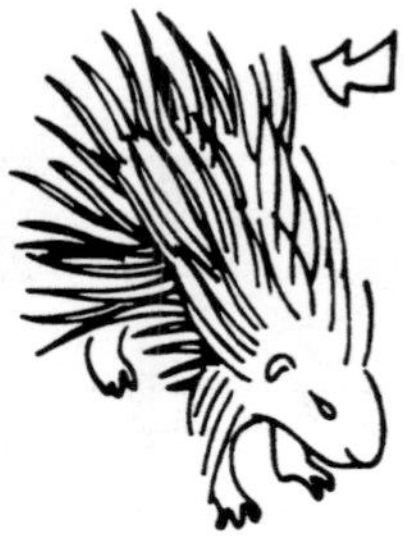 qu tr dr	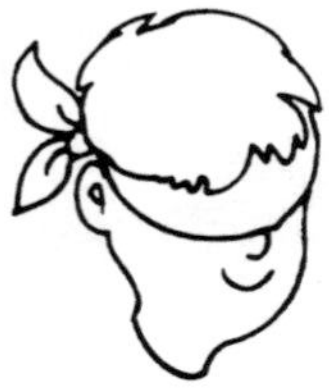 br cl bl	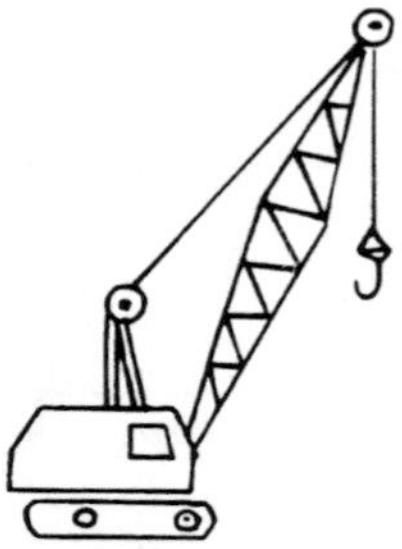 cr dr qu	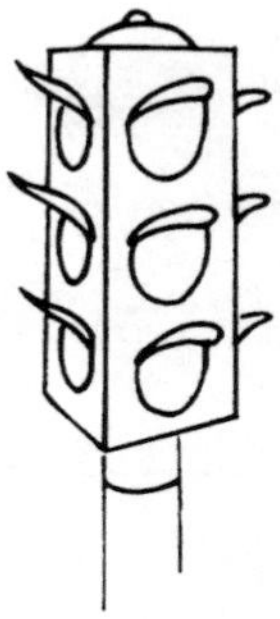 br tr cl
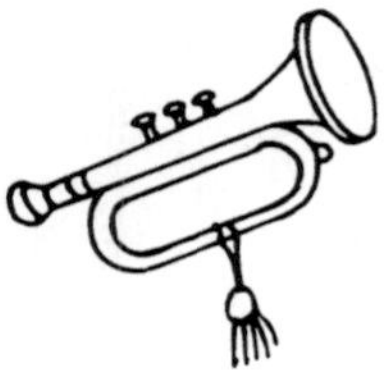 dr tr cr	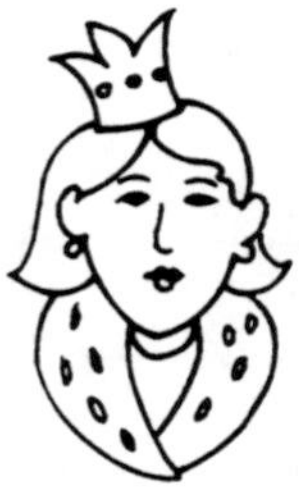 cl qu br	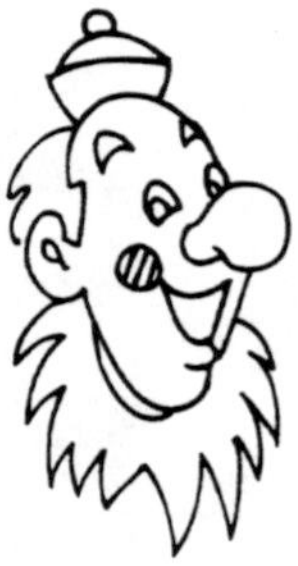 cr qu cl	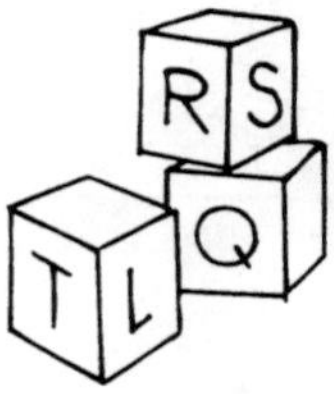 cl bl br
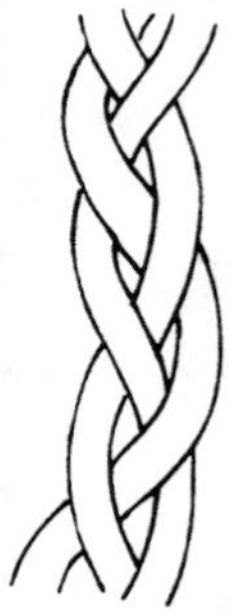 tr br dr	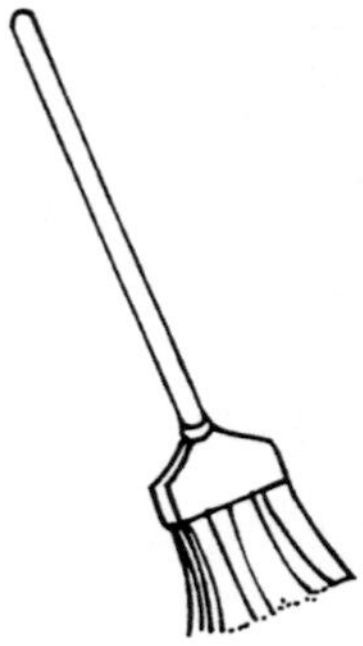 cl dr br	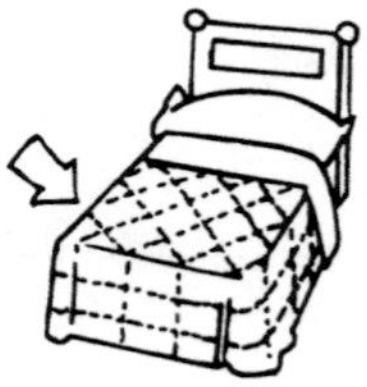 qu cr cl	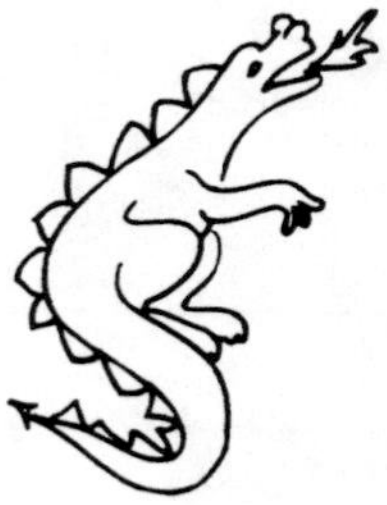 tr cl dr
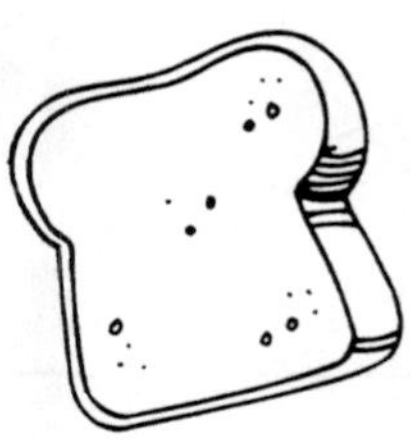 tr qu br	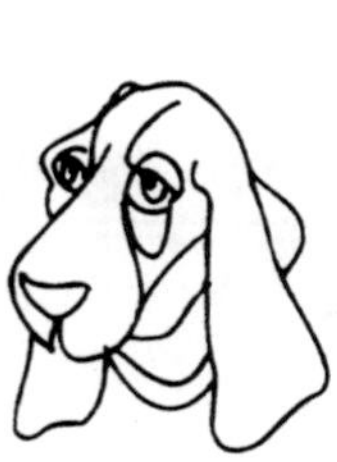 cl bl qu	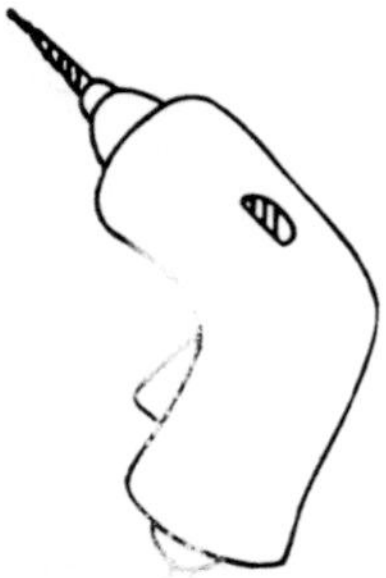 dr tr cl	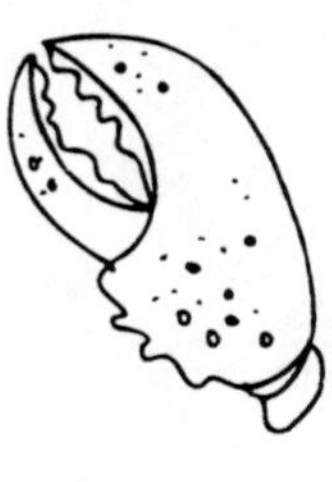 cl cr dr

Initial Sound of Blends FL, FR

Practice writing fl and fr on the lines. Then write fl or fr to show how the name of each picture begins.

fl ------------------

fr ------------------

MP341

Name _____   Date _____

Initial Sound of Blends GL, GR

Practice writing gl and gr on the lines. Then write gl or gr to show how the name of each picture begins.

MP3418

Initial Sound of Blends PL, PR

Practice writing **pl** and **pr** on the lines. Then write **pl** or **pr** to show how the name of each picture begins.

MP34

Name ______________________________ Date ______________

Review FL, FR, GL, GR, PL, PR

Circle the blend that begins the name of each picture below. The first one is done for you.

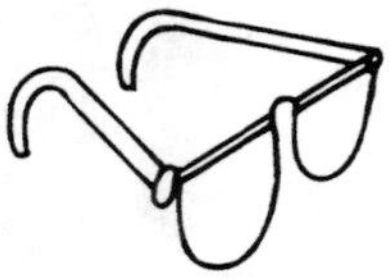 fr gr gl	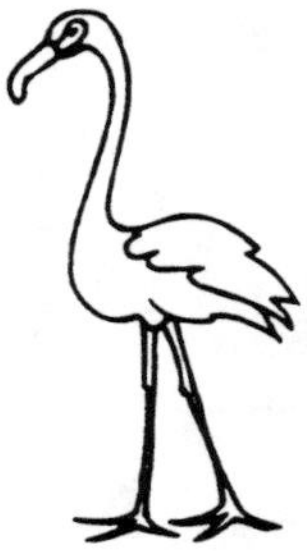 fl pr pl	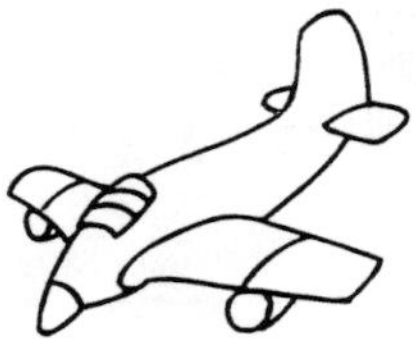 pr fl pl	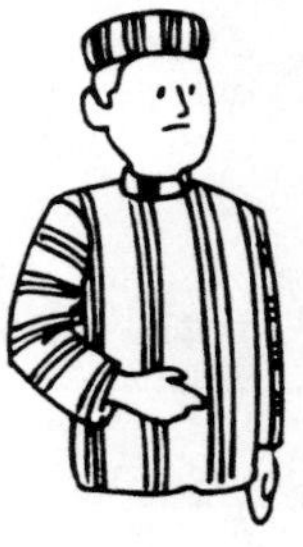 pr gr fr
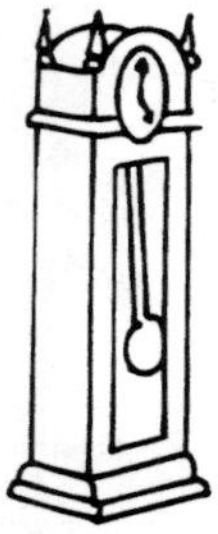 gr gl pr	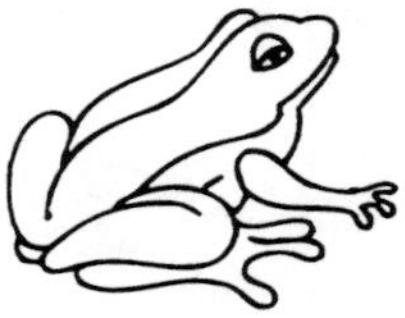 cr fr gl	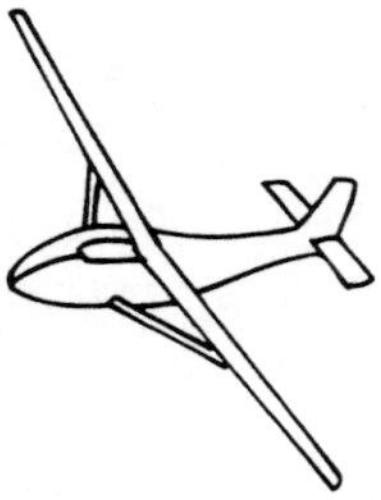 fl cl gl	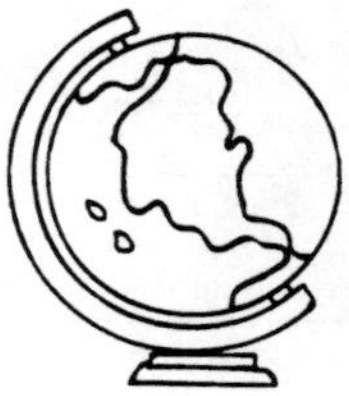 gl fl pl
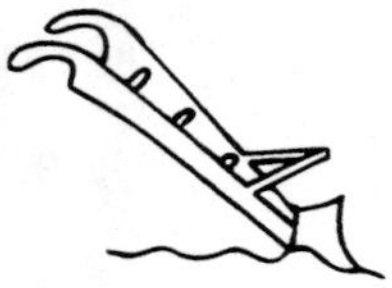 fl pl gl	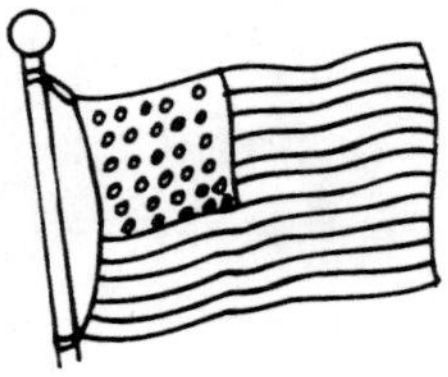 fr pl fl	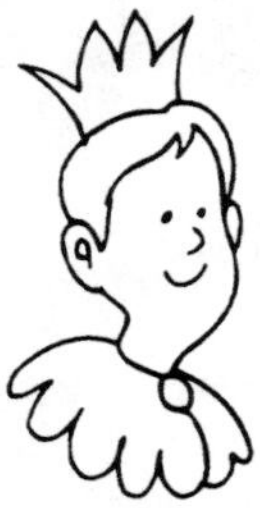 pr gr gl	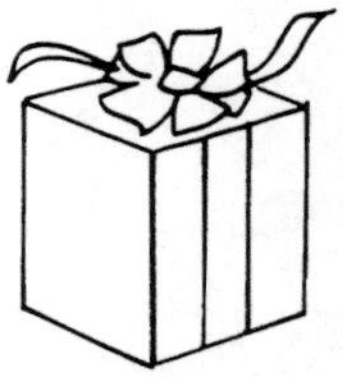 dr pl pr
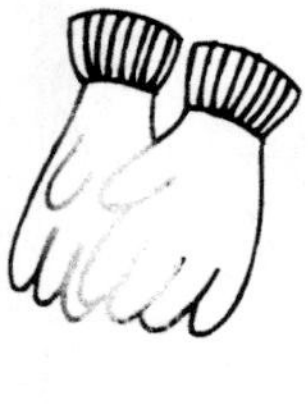 gl pr gr	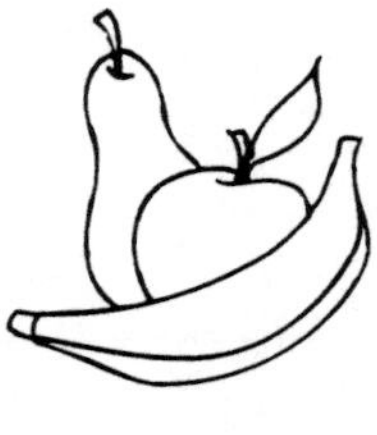 pl fr dr	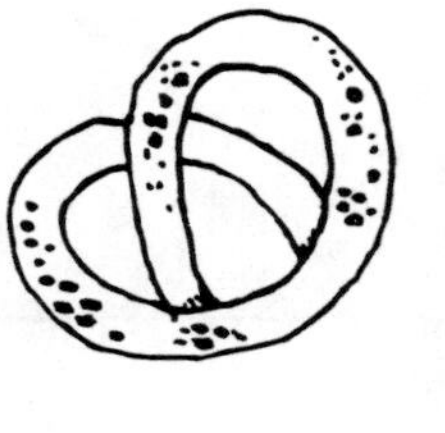 fr tr pr	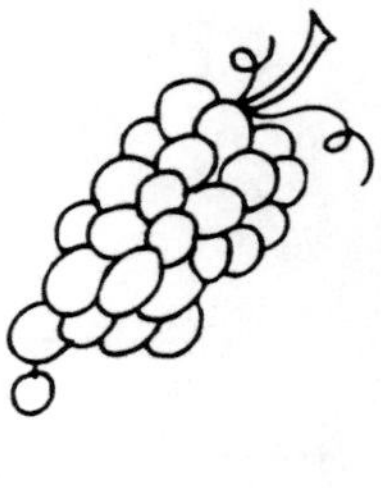 tr gr dr

Initial Sound of Blends SM, ST, SC, and SW

Write the blend that begins the name of each picture below.

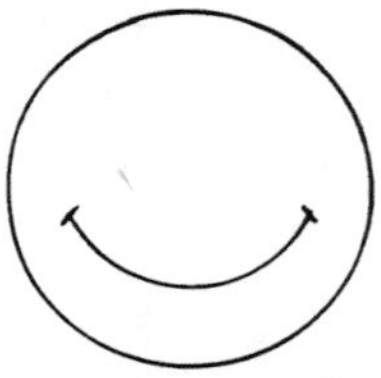

sm	st	sc	sw

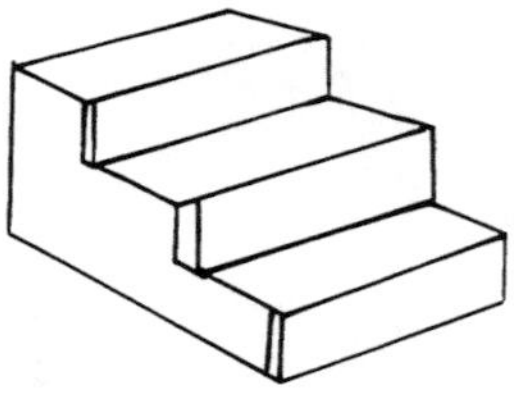

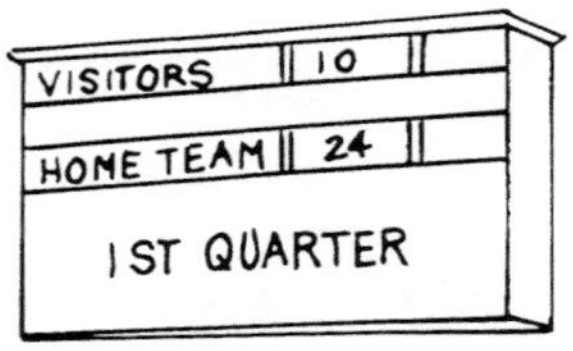

MP341

Name _____   Date _____

Initial Sound of Blends SN, SP, SK, and SL

Write the blend that begins the name of each picture below.

sn	sp	sk	sl

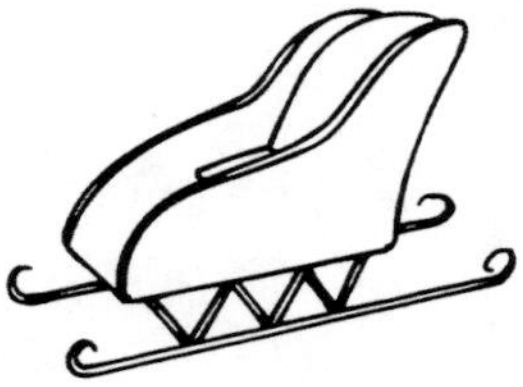

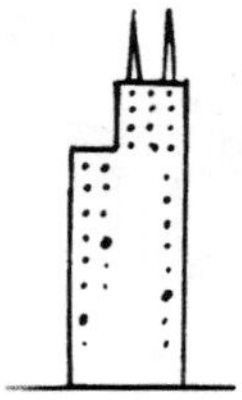

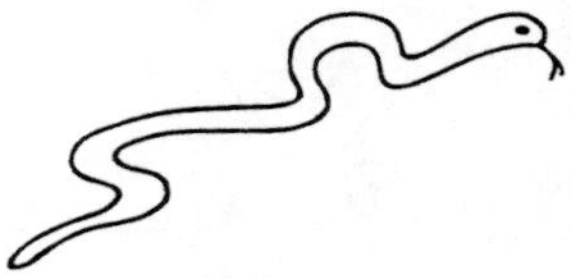

MP3418

Name _____ Date _____

Review Initial Blends

Write the blend that begins the name of each picture below.

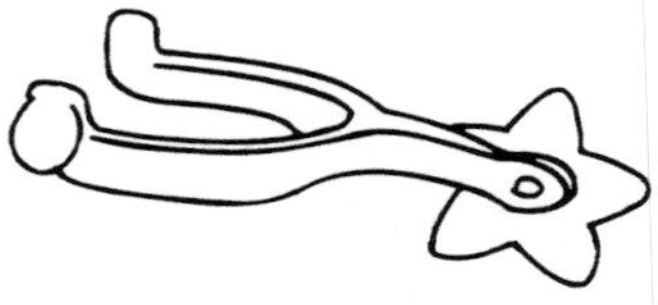

gl	pl	sp	cl

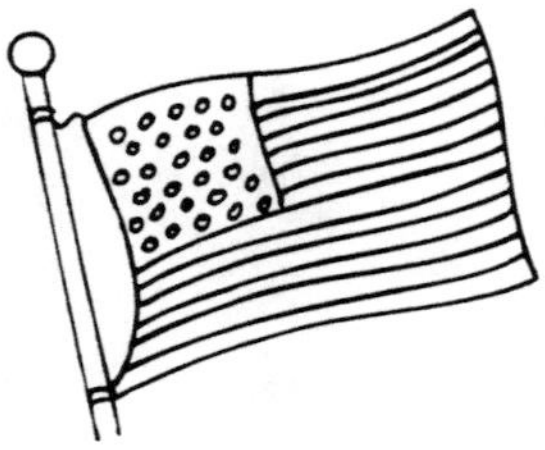

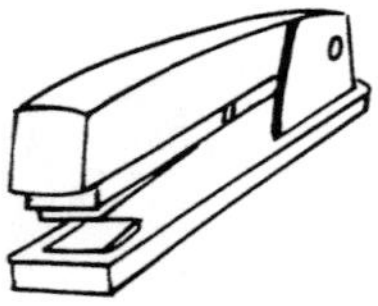

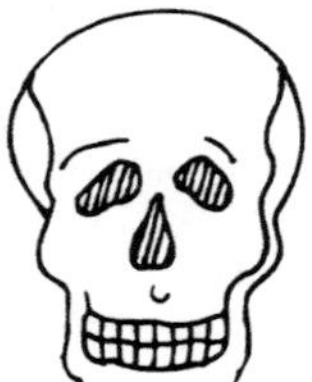

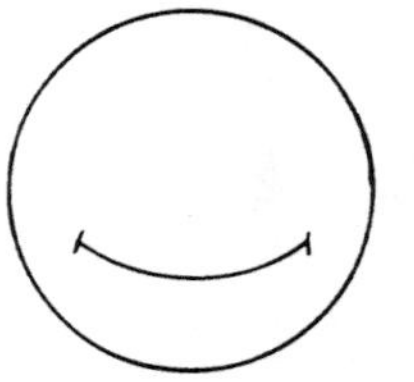

MP34

Name _____ Date _____

Review Initial Blends

Write the blend that begins the name of each picture below.

pr	sl	cr	qu

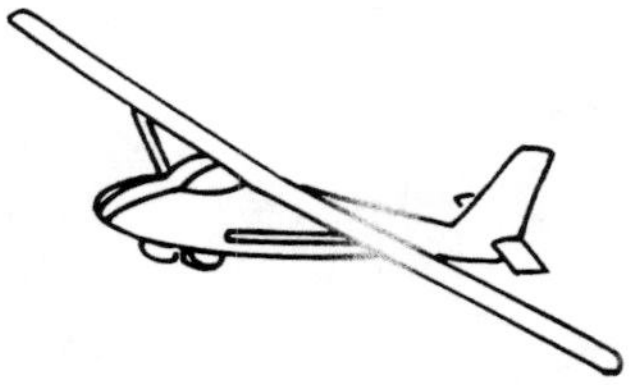

MP3418

Final Blend Sounds

Circle the blend that ends the name of each picture below. The first one is done for you.

nd (st) ft	lb rt sp	rd lt lk	mp nt rp
ld rm rk	lm sk rl	rn rf sm	mp nt rp
sp lm sk	rk ft rl	rm lf rn	lb mp ld
rd rf rb	lm nd nt	rk rm lk	rm rp mp

MP34

Name _____ Date _____

Final Blend Sounds

Write the blend that ends the name of each picture below.

lf	mp	rn	lk

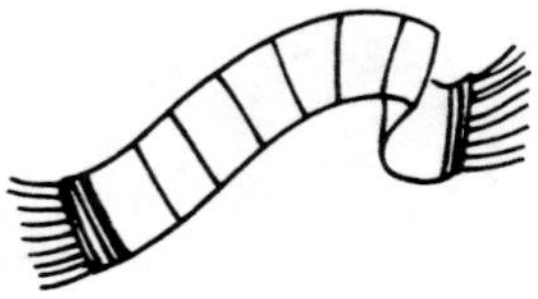

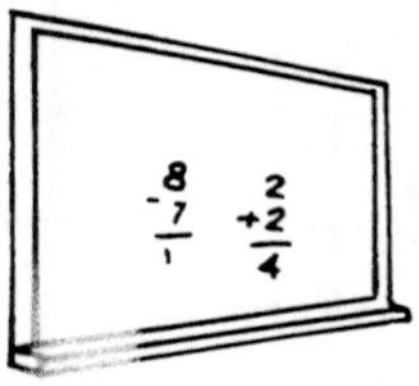

MP3418

Initial Sound of Digraph CH

Practice writing **ch** on the line. Then write **ch** below the picture whose name begins with **ch**.

ch ch

MP34

Initial Sound of Digraph SH

Practice writing **sh** on the line. Then write **sh** below the picture whose name begins with **sh**.

sh sh

Initial Sound of Digraphs TH and Wh

Practice writing **th** and **wh** on the lines. Then write **th** or **wh** below the picture whose name begins with **th** or **wh**.

MP34-

Name _____   Date _____

Review Initial Digraphs

Write the digraph that begins the name of each picture below.

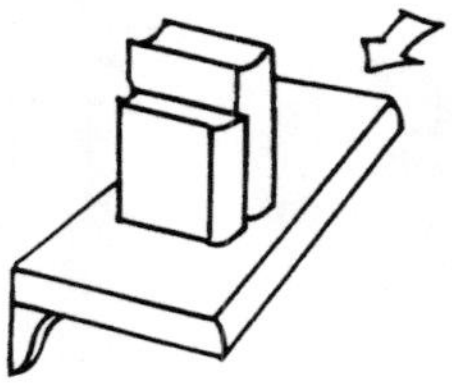

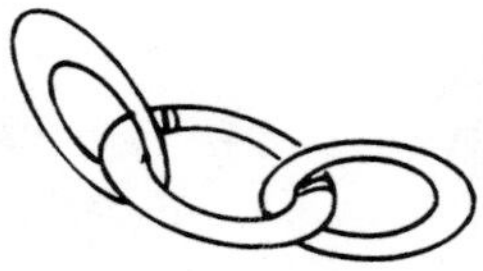

sh	th	ch	wh

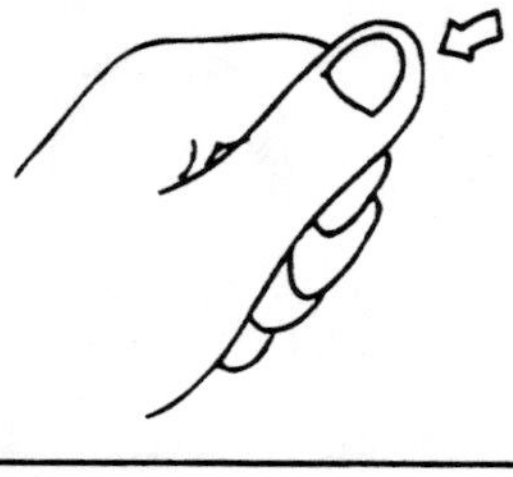

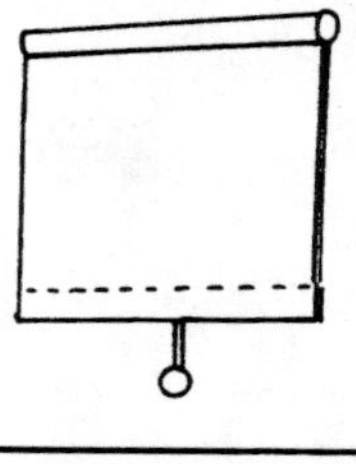

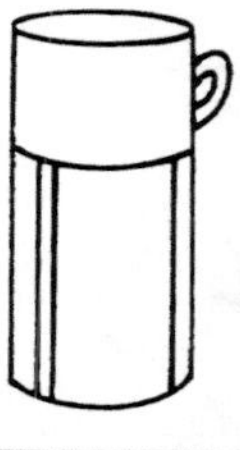

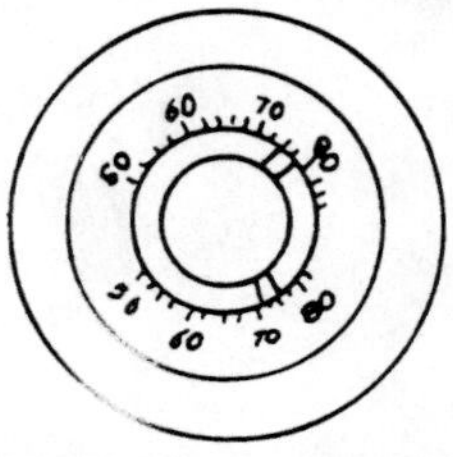

MP3418

Name _____ Date _____

Final Digraph Sounds

Write the digraph that ends the name of each picture below.

ch	sh	th	ck	ng	nk

MP34

Name _____   Date _____

Three-Letter Blends

Write the three-letter blend that begins or ends the name of each picture below.
Two are done for you.

str	thr		

MP3418

Review Initial Blends

Use words from the word box to complete the crossword puzzle.

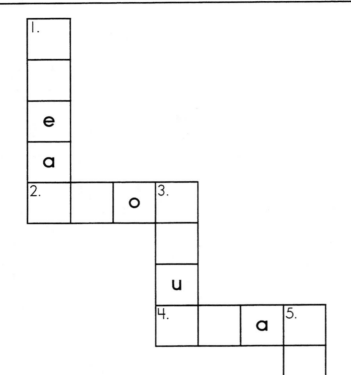

Down

1.

3.

5.

7.

Across

2.

4.

6.

8.

WORD LIST

scout	plug	tree	dress
bread	glad	drop	steam

MP341

Name _____   Date _____

Review Initial Blends and Digraphs

Use words from the word box to complete the crossword puzzle.

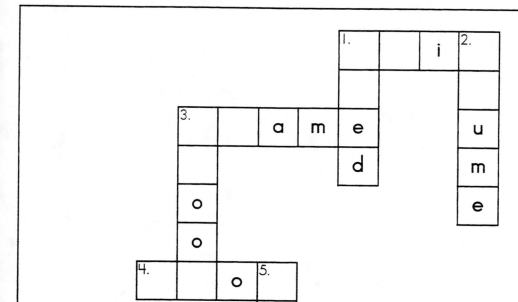

Down

1.

2.

3.

5.

7.

9.

Across

1.

3.

4.

6.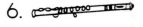

8.

WORD LIST

elf	grid	floor	crow	plume	flame
sled	whale	frog	flute	ship	

51

MP3418

Review Initial and Final Blends and Digraphs

Write the beginning and ending blends or digraphs in the spaces below.

b r oom   _ _ um   co l t   ta _ _

_ _ ib   _ _ us   ta _ _   ri _ _

_ _ oon   _ _ ize   ha _ _   la _ _

_ _ og   _ _ ep   hea _ _   mi _ _

Name _____ Date _____

Review Initial and Final Blends and Digraphs

Write the beginning and ending blends and digraphs in the spaces below.

b r u s h	_ _ i _ _	_ _ a _ _	_ _ o _ _
_ _ e _ _	_ _ i _ _	_ _ i _ _	_ _ ea _ _
_ _ a _ _	_ _ i _ _	_ _ u _ _	_ _ e _ _
3rd	_ _ i _ _	_ _ o _ _	_ _ a _ _	_ _ a _ _

MP3418

Review Initial and Final Blends and Digraphs

Cut out the words below. Paste each word under the matching picture.

block	drill	trunk	crash
skirt	brick	plant	footprint
check	lamp	scarf	churn

MP34

Name _____ Date _____

A Controlled by R Sound

Write **ar** under the name of each picture with this sound.

MP3418

Name _____   Date _____

O Controlled by R Sound

Write **or** under the name of each picture with this sound.

MP34

Name _____ Date _____

AR and OR Sounds

Write **ar** or **or** to complete each word.

yard   store

f ___ t   c ___   m ___ m   t ___ ch

th ___ n   y ___ n   f ___ ty   st ___

f ___ est   b ___ n   j ___   c ___ n

MP3418

Sounds of ER, IR, UR

Circle the words in the story with the er sound. Then write the words under the picture with the same spelling.

Annie, the girl with curls, was standing on the sidewalk waiting for her bus when there was a jerk on the hem of the skirt she was wearing. She felt fur rub against her leg. There was Perky, the family dog. He wanted to play, but the bus came and Annie got on it. The bus turned the corner and disappeared.

Annie was first to reach the classroom. She fed the gerbils, checked the dirt in the plants, and sat down to study the thirty verbs on the spelling test. She did not turn when the door opened, and the nurse came in to spray the room for germs. The spray burned Annie's eyes, so she went outside to stop the hurt.

fern   bird   purse

_____   _____   _____

_____   _____   _____

_____   _____   _____

_____   _____   _____

_____   _____   _____

_____   _____

_____

Name _____   Date _____

Diacritical Markings for R-Controlled Vowels

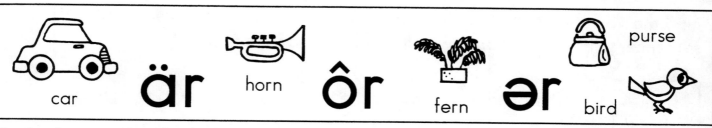

car **är** horn **ôr** fern **ər** purse bird

Circle the vowel-r sound you hear in the name of each picture.

är ôr ər	är ôr ər	är ôr ər	är ôr ər
är ôr ər	är ôr ər	är ôr ər	är ôr ər
är ôr ər	är ôr ər	är ôr ər	är ôr ər
är ôr ər	är ôr ər	är ôr ər	är ôr ər

59

MP3418

R-Controlled Sentences

Find the vowel-r word in the list that makes sense in each sentence. After the sentence, write the dictionary spelling for the vowel sound.

farm	1. The police car jumped the _____ during the chase. ____
park	2. Help me _____ the couch around, please. ____
scarf	3. The teacher gave a _____ test on Friday. ____
start	4. The bird sat on its _____ and sang. ____
corn	5. The man's _____ was ripped across the back. ____
form	6. My grandparents live on a _____. ____
porch	7. Cowboys drive _____ of cattle across the plains. ____
short	8. Sally used a _____ to keep her ears warm. ____
store	9. I had to _____ the sauce for ten minutes. ____
torn	10. Father went to _____ the car. ____
curb	11. The curtains were _____ beyond repair. ____
first	12. The front _____ was painted yesterday. ____
herds	13. Be sure your letter is in the correct _____. ____
nurse	14. The race will _____ at 2:00 p.m. ____
perch	15. The _____ was out of potatoes. ____
shirt	16. The _____ got the medicine from the shelf. ____
stir	17. The club meets the _____ Monday of every month. ____
turn	18. Wheat and _____ are the farmer's main crops. ____

MP341

EA Followed by R Sounds

The words below are spelled with the letters e-a-r. Write the words under the dictionary spelling that shows the sound they make.

bear	learn	ear	hear	earth	hearse
yearn	rear	wear	hearth	shear	tear
heart	swear	early	pear		

a(ə)r	i(ə)r	ər	är
_____	_____	_____	_____
_____	_____	_____	_____
_____	_____	_____	_____
	_____	_____	

Other words make these vowel sounds, too. Circle the words in each row that have the same vowel sounds. At the end of the row, write the correct vowel sound (a(ə)r, i(ə)r, ər, är).

learn	shear	turn	tear	bird	_____
glare	fair	carry	gear	heart	_____
hearse	stare	hearth	are	charm	_____
mere	learn	fear	steer	share	_____
early	fern	hearth	forth	yearn	_____
aren't	snare	frontier	lair	where	_____
their	here	they're	heart	there	_____

Write the vowel sound for the underlined words.

There was a <u>tear</u> in Mary's new dress. _____

Harris did not shed a <u>tear</u> when he fell off the fence. _____

How much money did we <u>earn</u> at the bake sale? _____

MP3418

Five Sounds of R-Control

The letter W in front of a vowel-r word can change the sound of the vowel. When W comes before **ar** as in warm, the **ar** makes the /ôr/ sound. When W comes before **or** as in worm, the **or** makes the /ər/ sound.

Write the words below in the puzzle that shows the matching sound in dictionary spelling. (Some words will be used with the puzzles on the next page.)

are	wart	world	wear	where	cheer	heart
tier	wary	chore	clear	steer	learn	hair
queer	march	merry	turn	sharp	fear	they're
here	herb	ears	dwarf	four	care	hearth
ear	worst	bird	fort	their	oar	art

MP341

Name _____   Date _____

Five Sounds Continued

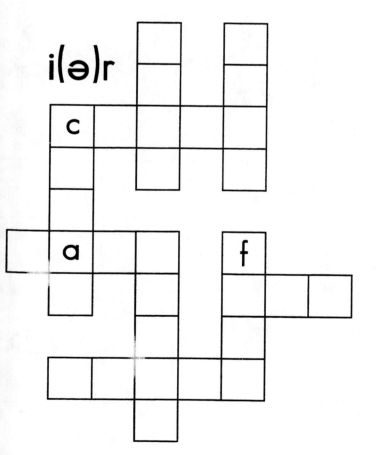

a(ə)r

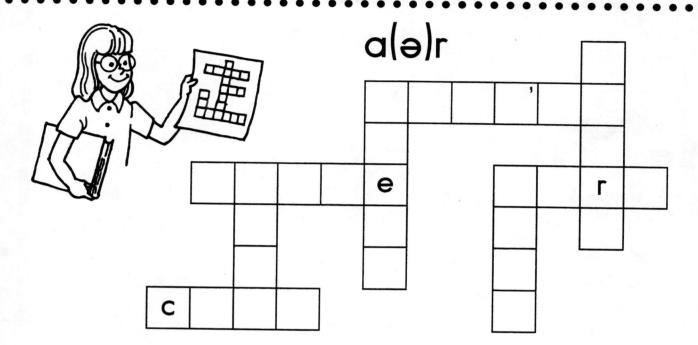

i(ə)r

ər

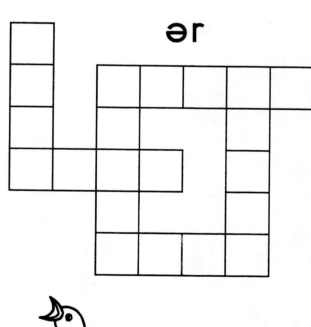

63

MP3418

Sounds of AU, AL, AW

Write the correct word under each picture. Underline the letters that help make the vowel sound au.

<u>au</u>tomobile

p<u>aw</u>

m<u>al</u>t

ch<u>alk</u>

laundry	saw
salt	ball
sausages	Australia
crawl	shawl

_ _

_ _

MP34

Sounds of OO

Circle the vowel sound you hear in each word.

book   goose

Name _____ Date _____

Sounds of OI

Circle the word that correctly completes each sentence.

toys

Oi

coins

	A _____ won the race.	boy boil
	The car needs _____.	soil oil
	The thunder made a loud _____.	enjoy noise
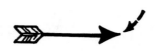	That _____ is sharp.	point poison
	Ted has three _____ trucks.	toil toy
	The water is _____.	boiling joining

MP341

AU, AL, AW, OO, OI Sounds

Write a word from the word box that correctly completes each sentence. The word should also have the vowel sound shown in ( ).

hook	loops	mood	royally
boots	call	zoom	stood
boiling	chalk	shawl	tools
hoof	mood	wood	hall

1. Grandma always kept a (ô) _____ on her shoulders.

2. The airplane made six (o͞o) _____ at the air show.

3. Don't ask him when he is in a bad (o͞o) _____.

4. The soldiers (o͝o) _____ at attention during the parade.

5. The teacher had to send to the office for some (ô) _____.

6. The king and queen were treated (oi) _____.

7. The horse stepped on a rock and hurt his (o͝o) _____.

8. The telephone (ô) _____ was long distance.

9. Sam's new (o͞o) _____ kept his feet dry in the snow.

10. The carpenter's (o͞o) _____ came in handy.

11. Hang the picture on the brass (o͝o) _____.

12. The water was (oi) _____ on the stove.

13. The principal made us line up in the (ô) _____ after recess.

14. We chopped (o͝o) _____ in the forest for a fire.

67

MP3418

Two Sounds of EA

Circle the word that has the same sound as each picture's name.

meadow	dream

meadow dream	meadow dream	meadow dream	meadow dream
meadow dream	meadow dream	meadow dream	meadow dream
meadow dream	meadow dream	meadow dream	meadow dream

MP34

Name _____ Date _____

Practicing Sounds of EA

Write words from the box in the column showing the matching **ea** sound. Two words will not fit in either column.

heavy	weak	jealous	measure	treadmill	clean	beast
feast	greasy	steak	weather	leader	deaf	measles
ready	healthy	peace	really	cream	dreadful	weaver
deadly	readiness	threaten	yeast	meant	great	pleasure
peach	cleanser	heaven	leave	wheat	reason	

ea as in meadow   **ea as in dream**

_____ _____   _____ _____

_____ _____   _____ _____

_____ _____   _____ _____

_____ _____   _____ _____

_____ _____   _____ _____

_____ _____   _____ _____

_____ _____   _____ _____

_____ _____   _____ _____

What two words did not fit in either column? _____ _____

What vowel sound does **ea** make in these two words? _____

MP3418

Name _____ Date _____

Sounds of IE Spelling

The letters **ie** together usually make the long **e** sound or the long **i** sound.

long e   The <u>thief</u> stole my pocketbook.
long i   The man <u>lied</u> about the money.

After each sentence below, write **thief** if the vowel sound in the underlined word is a long **e** sound. Write **lied** if the vowel sound in the underlined word is a long **i** sound.

1. The farmer's <u>field</u> was plowed and ready for planting. _____

2. Aunt Sally's <u>niece</u> came for a visit last summer. _____

3. We had hamburgers and french <u>fried</u> potatoes. _____

4. The traffic had to <u>yield</u> to pedestrians. _____

5. Martha <u>shrieked</u> when she saw a mouse. _____

6. The fresh flowers from the garden <u>died</u> before the party. _____

7. After church the <u>priest</u> greeted everyone. _____

8. Jeremy had roasted <u>wieners</u> at his party. _____

9. The children <u>tried</u> hard to keep the secret. _____

10. The Indian <u>chief</u> lead the dancers into the plaza. _____

11. Sometimes it is good to <u>believe</u> in miracles. _____

12. For Thanksgiving dinner we had turkey and pumpkin <u>pie</u>. _____

Some words spelled with **ie** make other sounds. Write short **i** or **e**, or long **u** after each sentence to tell the vowel sound of the underlined word.

The room had a beautiful <u>view</u> of the beach. ____

Bridgette and Tiffany were best <u>friends</u>. ____

MP341

Hearing Long and Short I, E, and Long U Sounds

Circle the words in each row that have the same vowel sounds.

1. shield   heat   bread   beast   lied
2. relive   beet   believe   health   thief
3. piece   please   relieve   feather   wild
4. sigh   signal   bead   cry   tied
5. friend   tried   cleanser   went   clean
6. tie   field   mild   kite   view
7. wish   view   mule   youth   chief
8. field   hint   inch   pill   tried
9. heaven   priest   meat   tied   queen
10. quilt   witch   lied   pin   piece
11. speech   bread   dream   pliers   wiener
12. coupon   you   through   time   priest
13. fried   piece   grief   thief   their
14. kind   hide   relieve   died   view

Explain the different ways one sound may be represented.

long e sound _____

long i sound _____

short e sound _____

short i sound _____

long u sound _____

MP3418

Puzzle of I and E Sounds

Complete the crossword using the vowel sounds in ( ) as clues. Choose your answers from the word box.

Across

1. Made from grain (ē)
4. A bird (ē)
5. A person who steals (ē)
7. A very small fellow (e)
8. Something that is done to bread (ē)
10. A delicious fruit (ē)
11. A metal (i)
12. To hit keys on a computer (ī)
13. A bird (e)

Down

1. Unable to see (ī)
2. Unable to hear (e)
3. A polite word (ē)
5. Something special (ē)
6. A big meal (ē)
8. Something to fly (ī)
9. Bashful (ī)

WORD BOX

| please | shy | wren | bread | knead | treat | blind | eagle |
| tin | peach | deaf | kite | type | feast | elf | thief |

MP3418

Exceptions to Rules

One expects to hear a short vowel sound in words like **kind**, **toll**, and **gold**.

Why? _____

One also expects to hear a short vowel sound in the word **baste**. Why?

_____

These words are exceptions to the rules. The consonant patterns that follow the vowels **a**, **o**, and **i** usually make the long vowel sounds, as they do in the above words.

Write each word from the word box after its definition. Use the vowel sounds in ( ) as clues.

WORD BOX			
kind	bold	taste	cold
gold	baste	hold	haste
paste	bind	waste	find
wind	knoll	told	toll

1. Quickness (ā) _____

2. Glue (ā) _____

3. A word that means very nice (ī) _____

4. A fee that must be paid to cross a bridge (ō) _____

5. You do this to a turkey when it is cooking (ā) _____

6. The opposite of warm (ō) _____

7. A shiny metal (ō) _____

8. Trash (ā) _____

9. Tie up securely (ī) _____

Which word above can be pronounced either with a long i or short i? _____

Write two sentences. Use the word both ways.

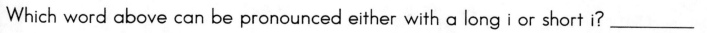

_____

_____

MP3418

Name _____   Date _____

Long O and OW

Circle **o** or **ou** to show which sound you hear in the picture's name.

 bow	ō	frown	ou
 ō ou	 ō ou	 ō ou	 ō ou
 ō ou	 ō ou	 ō ou	 ō ou
 ō ou	 ō ou	ō ou	cow ō ou

MP3418

OU Spelling and Its Sounds

Circle the word that correctly completes each sentence.

flowers

ou

houses

That is a pretty _____.

flower
flour

The _____ are white puffs in the sky.

clowns
clouds

We have a new _____.

couch
crown

My new dog is a _____.

Mouse
Chow

The baby is in its mother's _____.

plow
pouch

Father caught a _____.

town
trout

MP3418

Name _____   Date _____

Long O Puzzle

Complete the crossword puzzle with words that have the long ō sound.

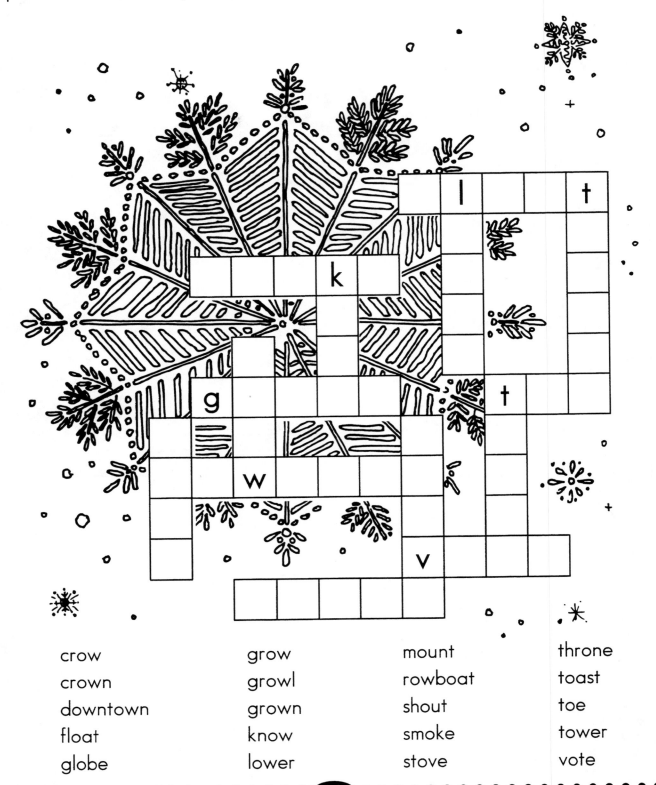

crow	grow	mount	throne
crown	growl	rowboat	toast
downtown	grown	shout	toe
float	know	smoke	tower
globe	lower	stove	vote

MP3418

OU Puzzle

Complete the crossword puzzle with words that have the **ou** sound.

bought	ground	mow	shout
brown	hour	owl	through
flower	house	round	trout
glow	lower	shoulder	town

MP3418

Name _____ Date _____

Sounds of OU Spelling

OU is a vowel digraph. It can make several sounds, as shown below. An example of each sound is given. Under each word is the mark for that sound, and another word with the same vowel sound, but spelled differently.

you	house	double	trough	doughnut	could
$\overline{oo}$	ou	u	au	$\bar{o}$	$\breve{oo}$
goose	owl	must	haul	bone	book

Write the sound marking for each word below. Circle the words with **ou**. Notice the different sounds **ou** can make.

ground ____	cough ____	tough ____
shawl ____	troll ____	shout ____
though ____	pouch ____	throw ____
towel ____	youth ____	stalk ____
thought ____	gown ____	soul ____
plow ____	growl ____	lunch ____
cloud ____	count ____	flow ____
sauce ____	shook ____	would ____
grown ____	bowl ____	mouse ____
ought ____	dough ____	trouble ____
shoe ____	jaw ____	bought ____
should ____	gold ____	hood ____
hoof ____	young ____	drum ____
found ____	tooth ____	rough ____
wool ____	soup ____	boat ____

MP341

Recognizing OU Spelling Sounds

Circle the words in the story that make one of the sounds shown. Spelling does not matter, only sound. If a word makes one of the six sounds below, circle it.

| $\overline{oo}$ | $\overline{oo}$ | u | au | ou | $\bar{o}$ |

After you circle the words, write each in the column under its sound notation.

Three hunters went into the jungle. They found footprints and decided to find out where they went. They noticed the tracks stopped at the base of a tree. A toucan sat on a bough and cawed. The hunters thought it was cawing at them, but then they looked in the tree and saw what had made the prints was sitting in the tree. A cougar was looking down at them with his big, round eyes. The hunters came to shoot, but when they had the chance they could not do it. They went home without it, and they were happy.

$\overline{oo}$	$\overline{oo}$	u	au	ou	$\bar{o}$
_____	_____	_____	_____	_____	_____
_____	_____	_____	_____	_____	_____
_____	_____	_____	_____	_____	_____
_____	_____	_____	_____	_____	_____
_____	_____	_____	_____	_____	_____
				_____	

MP3418

Name _____ Date _____

Spellings that Make the Sound Heard in Fool

Underline the words in each sentence that have the vowel sound heard in fool.

1. Students rescued the wounded kitten from a tree.
2. Mother bought cans of soup with coupons.
3. Father used glue and a screw to fix the picture frame.
4. The crew continued rowing after finishing first in the race.
5. The loon flew over blue Lake Mead.
6. The cook prepared goose for stew.
7. The baboon and cougar live at the zoo.
8. He told the truth about who threw a ball through the window.
9. The rooster crowed and the pigeon cooed.
10. The stew was tough and hard to chew.
11. The group ran a booth at the carnival.
12. He knew when he heard the cue to blow the whistle.
13. The clouds blew away and the sky was blue.
14. Hammers and screwdrivers are tools.
15. A few tulips bloomed before the last freezing spell.
16. We jumped into the blue pool.
17. The train was due at two o'clock.
18. The group's first clue was the loose gate.
19. He took the new stool to school.
20. The goose grew too big to stew.
21. Did you renew your overdue book?
22. Light from the moon threw light onto the dark streets.

What letter or letter combinations can make the sound heard in **fool**?

_____

MP341

OO and O Puzzles

Use the words at the bottom of the page to complete each puzzle. Write each word in the puzzle with the matching vowel sound. All words will not be used.

cue	gold	view	throw	choose
how	blow	foil	float	cougar
hue	plow	most	growl	smooth
sew	soul	home	tough	though
crew	truth	two	should	toucan

MP3418

Name _____ Date _____

Award

CONGRATULATIONS

_____:

You have achieved an important goal!

You have learned about special sounds, blends, and digraphs, and special vowels.

Good Job!

Signed _____

Date _____

MP34

Answer Key

Page 1

question

quarterback

queen

quarter

quotation marks

quill

Page 2

socks	six	ducks	fox
box	jacks	ax	kicks
oxen	exit	sixty	necks

Page 3

celery, s

calculator, k

faucet, s

candles, k

comb, k

cupcake, k

corn, k

cemetery, s

centipede, s

pencil, s

camel, k

carrot, k

camera, k

calendar, k

cent, s

candy, k

castle, k

mice, s

cymbals, s

fence, s

Page 4

Courtney, could, climb, <u>recess</u>, could, because, soccer, <u>bounced</u>, Courtney's, Curt, Carl, caught, carefully, <u>fence</u>, <u>Nancy</u>, carried, <u>center</u>, <u>circle</u>, continued, o'clock, clanged, <u>science</u>

cages, <u>mice</u>, blocked, <u>entrance</u>, <u>science</u>, class, second, <u>encyclopedias</u>, instructor, close, <u>face</u>, <u>voices</u>, <u>place</u>, clear, <u>cerise</u>, <u>center</u>, section, caused, reaction, <u>decided</u>, particles, collide, color, instructed, class, record, card, cabinet

Page 5

1. seen
2. scene
3. cent
4. scissors
5. scenery
6. scissor
7. scents
8. scent
9. science
10. scenic

cent, scent, sent

sense, cents, scents

scene, seen

Page 6

gum, g

goat, g

hinge, j

goose, g

gift, g

giraffe, j

girl, g

gym, j

engine, j

gate, g

ghost, g

gown, g

gas, g

giant, j

grass, g

grid, g

egg, g

game, g

bridge, j

garden, g

Page 7

1. <u>great</u>, <u>gathered</u>, <u>green</u>   G
2. <u>gentle</u> <u>giant</u>   J
3. <u>gavel</u>, <u>group</u>   G
4. <u>marriage</u>, <u>carriage</u>, <u>lodge</u>   J
5. <u>hinge</u>, <u>cage</u>   J
6. <u>green</u>, <u>garden</u>, <u>grew</u>   G
7. <u>gorilla</u>, <u>growled</u>, <u>against</u>   G
8. <u>goldfish</u>, <u>golden</u>, <u>glass</u>   G
9. <u>large</u>, <u>page</u>   J
10. <u>juggling</u>, <u>grapefruits</u>   G
11. <u>goldfish</u>, <u>guppies</u>, <u>together</u>   G
12. <u>bingo</u>, <u>game</u>   G
13. <u>goblins</u>, <u>ghosts</u>   G
14. <u>guest</u>, <u>going</u>, <u>rag</u>   G
15. <u>glass</u>, <u>goblet</u>   G
16. <u>geology</u>, <u>gems</u>   J
17. <u>orange</u>, <u>bridge</u>   J
18. <u>huge</u>, <u>engine</u>, <u>gently</u>   J
19. <u>gentleman</u>, <u>bridge</u>, <u>barge</u>   J
20. <u>gopher</u>, <u>gorilla</u>   G

MP3418

Answer Key

Page 8

giant
sixty-six
officer
giraffe
quill
dancer
oxen
grocery cart
general
gorilla
equal
garbage

city
garage
circle
calf
gypsy
gems
engine
liquid

Page 9

S says /s/
that's
castle
question
Susie
listen

C says /s/
cellar
ice cream
cyclone
exercise
certificate

K says /k/
kettle
hanky
spiked
poker

C says /k/
calcium
excuse
cucumber
crystal
secret

J says /j/
banjo
jockey
major
majority

G says /j/
garage
bandage
gentle
geography

G says /g/
guest
goblet
gloves
tiger

S says /z/
races
cousin
easy
wise

Page 10

knife
knee
nickel
knitting
needle
knocker
gnome
necklace
knapsack
newspaper
knuckles
knot
gnat
knickers
knob
gnu

Page 11

tough, thought, weighed, fights, laugh, fight, through, night, laughed, caught, thigh, fought, taught, height, weight, high

1. though, bought, ought, dough
2. Sentences will vary. The words to be used: cough, rough, trough

The **gh** is at the beginning. You can hear /g/.
The h is silent.

Page 12

1. dolphins, favorites
2. football, autographed
3. pheasants, five
4. Phonics, alphabet's
5. elephant's, tough
6. Father fixed, fence, gopher, from, flowers
7. trophy for physical fitness
8. Physicians
9. triumphant, for, fifth
10. phantom, Friday
11. laughed, frisky
12. Father, rough
13. sphere
14. from, orphanage
15. trough, farm

MP3418

Answer Key

16. <u>ph</u>rase, o<u>ft</u>en
17. or<u>ph</u>an, <u>ph</u>ysical, cou<u>gh</u>
18. <u>F</u>ive, <u>f</u>ailed, <u>ph</u>ysics
19. lau<u>gh</u>ed, <u>f</u>ilm
20. gra<u>ph</u>, <u>f</u>ifty, <u>f</u>armers
21. telegra<u>ph</u>
22. <u>ph</u>otogra<u>ph</u>er
23. <u>Ph</u>ysical, <u>f</u>avorite

f, ph, gh

Page 13

Across

1. f, leaf
4. f, raft
8. gh, cough
9. gh, trough
11. gh, laugh
12. gh, rough
13. ph, elephant
15. f, after
16. ph, graph

Down

2. f, finger
3. gh, enough
5. f, awful
6. ph, phone
7. ph, orphan
10. f, furnace
14. ph, phrase

Page 14

/z/ **Across**   **Down**

treason   reason
those   his

/sh/ **Across**   **Down**

mission   tissue
pressure   Russian

/zh/ **Across**   **Down**

usual   vision
leisure   casual

Page 15

/ch/ **Across**   **Down**

3. church   1. chop
                 2. chain
                 4. ranch

/k/ **Across**   **Down**

3. orchestra   1. orchid
                 2. ache

/sh/ **Across**   **Down**

1. champagne   1. charades
4. machine   2. parachute
                 3. chef

Page 16

ambitious, impression, actions, machines, shake, attention, invention, machinery, action, distraction essential, injections, precious, Charlotte, She, shot, impression, sharp, assured, insurance hesitation, finishing, tenacious, special, tissue, protection, facial, expression, section, determination

<u>tion</u>   **<u>sh</u>**

actions   shake
attention   She
invention   shot
action   sharp
distraction
injections   **<u>ti</u>**
hesitation   ambitious
protection   essential
section
determination   **<u>ch</u>**
                 machines
<u>ci</u>   machinery
precious   Charlotte
tenacious
special   **<u>s</u>**
facial   assured
finishing   insurance
                 tissue
<u>sion</u>
impression
impression
expression

MP3418

Answer Key

Page 17

pic~~t~~ure
depar~~t~~ure
frac~~t~~ure
crea~~t~~ure
pas~~t~~ure
mois~~t~~ure
situa~~t~~ion
mu~~t~~ual
actua~~ll~~y
den~~t~~ures
fac~~t~~ually
~~s~~anctuaries
U after t usually says /ch/ as in **vulture**.

Page 18

lam~~b~~	~~k~~not	~~w~~rist	com~~b~~
si~~g~~n	cha~~l~~k	~~w~~ren	li~~gh~~t
ca~~l~~f	thum~~b~~	~~gh~~ost	fi~~gh~~t
~~g~~nat	~~k~~nob	crum~~b~~s	ha~~l~~f

Page 19

~~k~~ni~~gh~~t	fi~~gh~~t	li~~gh~~t	ni~~gh~~t
~~w~~res~~t~~le	this~~t~~le	whis~~t~~le	cas~~t~~le
~~k~~nit	~~k~~nob	~~k~~nife	~~k~~nee
~~w~~ren	~~w~~rite	~~w~~reath	~~w~~rist
bom~~b~~	lam~~b~~	com~~b~~	thum~~b~~

Page 20

ha~~l~~f	b~~ui~~lding	crum~~b~~s	tong~~ue~~
cas~~t~~le	s~~w~~ord	si~~g~~n	glas~~s~~
ya~~ch~~t	~~k~~night	s~~c~~issors	~~w~~reath
slei~~gh~~	~~w~~restler	cra~~c~~k	~~g~~nome

Page 21

W

~~w~~ring	~~w~~rangler	~~w~~rench	~~w~~rinkle	~~w~~rap
~~w~~restle	~~w~~rung	~~w~~rong	~~w~~ritten	~~w~~reath

G and **gh**

fri~~gh~~ten	si~~g~~n	hei~~gh~~t	sli~~gh~~t	hi~~gh~~
wei~~gh~~t	deli~~gh~~t	bri~~gh~~t	wei~~gh~~	strai~~gh~~t

T

ma~~t~~ch	cru~~t~~ch	sti~~t~~ch	wi~~t~~ch	la~~t~~ch
hu~~t~~ch	twi~~t~~ch	pa~~t~~ch	di~~t~~ch	swi~~t~~ch

D

ju~~dg~~e	lo~~dg~~e	tru~~dg~~e	le~~dg~~e	smu~~dg~~e
ple~~dg~~e	he~~dg~~e	do~~dg~~e	gru~~dg~~e	e~~dg~~e
nec~~k~~	gras~~s~~	cuf~~f~~	duc~~k~~	hal~~l~~
eg~~g~~	mit~~t~~	kic~~k~~	loc~~k~~	jac~~ks~~
glas~~s~~	dec~~k~~			

Page 22

fli~~gh~~t	com~~b~~	g~~u~~est
lis~~t~~en	h~~ou~~rs	~~w~~rong
ha~~l~~f	si~~g~~n	brea~~d~~
thum~~b~~	has~~t~~en	~~g~~nome
clim~~b~~	sta~~l~~k	recei~~p~~t
ta~~l~~k	~~k~~nave	cas~~t~~le
di~~t~~ch	craw~~l~~	lam~~b~~
paint	whis~~t~~le	corp~~s~~
cha~~l~~k	s~~c~~ience	slei~~gh~~
ya~~ch~~t	s~~w~~ord	ans~~w~~er
bri~~dg~~e	~~k~~neel	~~w~~rist
bisc~~u~~it	bri~~gh~~t	~~w~~rap
~~w~~ring	p~~s~~alm	ba~~t~~ch
glis~~t~~en	ca~~l~~m	ca~~l~~f
campai~~g~~n	co~~a~~t	bom~~b~~
~~w~~restle	clif~~f~~	gro~~w~~
friend	mi~~gh~~t	~~w~~rite
crayon	mois~~t~~en	~~g~~naw
antiq~~ue~~	~~k~~new	t~~w~~o
num~~b~~	~~w~~ren	ei~~gh~~t

Page 23

răn	kärt	stak
skärf	laf	kôrd
king	raft	thēnk
hinj	juj	kīt
tha(ə)r	fərn	wauch
chauk	haf	chärm
pēs	dīd	härt
kwilt	wich	reskū
rənch	frənd	lam
sizər	märch	kwīət
wôrm	shelf	wərld
rōoən	kwiz	shank
chōoz	lərn	līən

MP3418

Answer Key

Page 24

crab	smell	box
gym	ours	baby
goal	seat	gnome
phone	climb	chef
fight	cough	wren
knob	stalk	numb
quick	edge	palm
rough	crawl	grow
paste	cuff	please
ferry	fence	action
sign	love	sure
quite	mean	who
lift	meant	crust

Page 25

Who is the paragraph about? <u>the Pilgrims</u>
Why did they come to America? <u>because they wanted to practice their religion</u>
When did they leave England? <u>September 1620</u>
How long did it take them to make the trip? <u>three months</u>
How many passengers were on the Mayflower? <u>103</u>

Page 26

The modern Olympic Games were first held in Athens, Greece, in 1896. One of the main goals of the games was to promote better international understanding and cooperation through a universal medium—athletics.

The ancient Greek Olympic Games had much the same in mind when they began over twenty-seven hundred years ago. Now over one hundred nations compete in the summer and winter games.

Page 27

<u>The</u> stacho͞o uv libərtē haz sto͝od az ə simbəl uv frēdəm in no͞o yôrk's härbər sins 1886. It wuz givən to͞o əma(ə)rəkə bī <u>the</u> french guvərnmənt az ə simbəl uv frendship bētwēn <u>the</u> to͞o kuntrēz. <u>The</u> grāt lādē welkəmd milyənz uv iməgrənts to͞o <u>the</u> no͞o kuntrē hwen <u>the</u> ships aun hwich <u>thā</u> wər əriving sāld past hər aun tha(ə)r wā to͞o eləs īlənd. Not as menē iməgrənts pas <u>the</u> stacho͞o to͞odā bēcəz <u>the</u> no͞okumərz ərīv bī plān.

Page 28

cu<u>ff</u>	dre<u>ss</u>	e<u>gg</u>	pa<u>ss</u>
hi<u>ll</u>	mi<u>tt</u>	do<u>ll</u>	ba<u>ss</u>
gla<u>ss</u>	mu<u>ff</u>	dri<u>ll</u>	bu<u>zz</u>
bu<u>ll</u>	gu<u>ll</u>	ki<u>ss</u>	gra<u>ss</u>

Page 29

dropper	drum	dress
drill	dragon	dresser

Page 30

trombone	tree	tricycle	truck
trampoline	trophy	triangle	
trap	trunk	trumpet	

Page 31

bread, br	blindfold, bl
bride, br	bronco, br
blocks, b	brick, br
blastoff, bl	bridge, br
brush, br	briefcase, br
bloodhound, bl	bloomers, bl

Page 32

cradle, cr	crayons, cr
crow, cr	clip, cl
clock, cl	crib, cr
crocodile, cr	clarinet, cl
claw, cl	crown, cr
cracker, cr	clown, cl

Page 33

qu, quill	cr, crane
tr, trumpet	cl, clown
br, braid	qu, quilt
br, bread	dr, drill
bl, blindfold	tr, traffic light
qu, queen	bl, blocks
br, broom	dr, dragon
bl, bloodhound	cl, claw

Page 34

frying pan, fr	flamingo, fl
flashlight, fl	french horn, fr
freckles, fr	frame, fr
fruit, fr	flag, fl

MP3418

Answer Key

frown, fr
flute, fl

fly, fl
float, fl

Page 35

gloves, gl
grandfather clock, gr
grave, gr
grades, gr
globe, gl
greenhouse, gr

graduate, gr
grapes, gr
grill, gr
glue, gl
grass, gr
glider, gl

Page 36

present, pr
platter, pl
prisoner, pr
plaid, pl
prince, pr
pretzel, pr

plane, pl
prism, pr
propeller, pr
planets, pl
prize, pr
platypus, pl

Page 37

gl, glasses
gr, grandfather clock
pl, plow
gl, gloves
fl, flamingo
fr, frog
fl, flag
fr, fruit

pl, plane
gl, glider
pr, prince
pr, pretzel
pr, prisoner
gl, globe
pr, present
gr, grapes

Page 38

smile, sm
scorpion, sc
sweater, sw
scout, sc
star, st
swan, sw
stairs, st
scarf, sc

scarecrow, sc
stove, st
score, sc
smoke, sm
swim, sw
scoop, sc
stick, st
stag, st

Page 39

snowman, sn
snail, sn
sleeping bag, sl
spaceman, sp
spoon, sp

skate, sk
sled, sl
skyscraper, sk
slate, sl
slide, sl

skeleton, sk
spear, sp
sneakers, sn

spider, sp
sling, sl
snake, sn

Page 40

globe, gl
flag, fl
stapler, st
blizzard, bl
pliers, pl
ski, sk
crib, cr
swim, sw

spur, sp
present, pr
grand piano, gr
skull, sk
club, cl
queen, qu
train, tr
smile, sm

Page 41

prisoner, pr
clown, cl
swan, sw
drink, dr
sling, sl
tricycle, tr
glider, gl
quail, qu

crayons, cr
skateboard, sk
planets, pl
drainer, dr
quarter, qu
blastoff, bl
bridle, br
scarecrow, sc

Page 42

st, ghost
ld, blindfold
sp, wasp
rd, sword
rt, cart
lm, film
ft, raft
nt, footprint

lt, belt
sm, prism
lf, shelf
lk, milk
rp, harp
nd, merry-go-round
lb, bulb
mp, lamp

Page 43

elf, lf
dart, rt
salt, lt
chalkboard, rd
lamp, mp
hand, nd
scarf, rf
blizzard, rd

yarn, rn
question mark, rk
shirt, rt
pump, mp
elk, lk
mask, sk
bloodhound, nd
present, nt

MP3418

Answer Key

Page 44

chain	cheetah
chief	chess
chicken	chair
church	check
chimney	chart

Page 45

shadow	ship
sheep	shack
shower	shoe
shell	shirt
shade	shelf

Page 46

whale, wh	thirteen, th
wheat, wh	thermos, th
thongs, th	thumb, th
thermometer, th	thief, th
thorn, th	wharf, wh
whistle, wh	whip, wh

Page 47

shelf, sh	chain, ch
sheep, sh	shadow, sh
chicken, ch	thumb, th
thermos, th	shark, sh
thirty seven, th	whale, wh
shovel, sh	thimble, th
chair, ch	shade, sh
whistle, wh	thermostat, th

Page 48

crash, sh	beach, ch
brush, sh	stick, ck
sling, ng	moth, th
ring, ng	breath, th
clock, ck	brick, ck
peach, ch	duck, ck

Page 49

strawberry, str	scribble, scr
shrub, shr	stroller, str
spring, spr	throat, thr
witch, tch	arch, rch
thread, thr	sprinkler, spr
splash, spl	church, rch
shrimp, shr	watch, tch
world, rld	crutch, tch

Page 50

Across
2. drop
4. glad
6. scout
8. steam

Down
1. bread
3. plug
5. dress
7. tree

Page 51

Across
1. ship
3. flame
4. crow
6. flute
8. frog

Down
1. sled
2. plume
3. floor
5. whale
7. elf
9. grid

Page 52

br, broom	lt, colt
cr, crib	ck, tack
sp, spoon	nd, hand
fr, frog	rt, heart
dr, drum	nk, tank
pl, plus	ng, ring
pr, prize	mp, lamp
st, step	lk, milk

MP3418

Answer Key

Page 53

brush

check

trash

third

swing

drink

shirt

thorn

flask

sling

thumb

wharf

clock

breath

shelf

shark

Page 54

crash

print

drill

skirt

trunk

brick

check

plant

prism

block

churn

lamp

Page 55

harp   scarf   ark

cart   barn   star

car   dart   card

arch   jar   yarn

Page 56

fork

horse

shorts

corn

torn

horn

fort

storm

sore

forty

stork

core

store

Page 57

fort

thorn

forest

car

yarn

barn

arm

forty

jar

torch

star

corn

Page 58

fern   bird   purse

her   girl   curls

jerk   skirt   curb

her   first   fur

Perky   dirt   turned

gerbils   thirty   curve

verbs   turn

germs   nurse

                burned

                hurt

Page 59

dart, är

herd, er

shirt, er

spurs, er

girl, er

storm, ôr

barn, är

cards, är

horse, ôr

nurse, er

curve, er

forty, ôr

target, är

corn, ôr

fern, er

first, er

Page 60

1. curb, er
2. turn, er
3. short, ôr
4. perch, er
5. shirt, er
6. farm, är
7. herds, er
8. scarf, är
9. stir, er
10. park, är
11. torn, ôr
12. porch, ôr
13. form, ôr
14. start, är
15. store, ôr
16. nurse, er
17. first, er
18. corn, ôr

Page 61

a(ə)r   i(ə)r

bear   ear

wear   hear

swear   rear

pear   shear

        fear

MP3418

Answer Key

ər	är
learn	hearth
earth	heart
hearse
yearn
early

learn, turn, bird, ər
glare, fair, carry, a(ə)r
hearth, are, charm, är
mere, fear, steer, i(ə)r
early, fern, yearn, ər
snare, lair, where, a(ə)r
their, they're, there, a(ə)r
tear, a(ə)r
tear, i(ə)r
earn, ər

Page 62
ar
Across: hearth, march, art
Down: are, heart, sharp

or
Across: oar, four, fort
Down: chore, dwarf, wart

Page 63
a (e) r
Across: they're, where, wary, care
Down: hair, their, wear, merry

i (e) r
Across: cheer, ears, ear, queer
Down: tier, here, clear, steer, fear

er
Across: world, bird, turn
Down: herb, worst, learn

Page 64
crawl | laundry | shawl | saw
Australia | salt | ball | sausages

Page 65
moon, o͞o | hoof, o͝o | wood, o͝o | hoop, o͞o
hook, o͝o | hood, o͝o | tooth, o͞o | moose, o͞o
cook, o͝o | wool, o͝o | stool, o͞o | food, o͞o

Page 66
boy, oil, noise, point, toy, boiling

Page 67
1. shawl
2. loops
3. mood
4. stood
5. chalk
6. royally
7. hoof
8. call
9. boots
10. tools
11. hook
12. boiling
13. hall
14. wood

Page 68
chest, meadow | thread, meadow
teacher, dream | head, meadow
beaver, dream | pheasant, meadow
seal, dream | beagle, dream
beak, dream | feather, meadow
eagle, dream | bead, dream

Page 69
ea as in meadow

heavy | jealous
deaf | healthy
readiness | meant
cleanser | ready
dreadful | measure
threaten | weather
heaven | deadly
pleasure | treadmill

91

MP3418

Answer Key

ea as in dream

clean	wheat
cream	peace
reason	peach
feast	leader
measles	really
weak	beast
greasy	yeast
leave	weaver

great, steak
the a sound, a

Page 70

1. thief	7. thief
2. thief	8. thief
3. lied	9. lied
4. thief	10. thief
5. thief	11. thief
6. lied	12. lied

u, e

Page 71

1. shield, heat, beast
2. beet, believe, thief
3. piece, please, relieve
4. sigh, cry, tied
5. friend, cleanser, went
6. tie, mild, kite
7. view, mule, youth
8. hint, inch, pill
9. priest, meat, queen
10. quilt, witch, pin
11. speech, dream, wiener
12. coupon, you, through
13. piece, grief, thief
14. kind, hide, died

long e

vowel combinations ea, ie, ee

long i

vowel combination ie, y
i-consonant-e
i followed by g, gh, ld, nd

short e

ie, ea, e as only vowel in beginning or middle

short i

ie, i as only vowel in beginning or middle

long u

ou, iew, ew, u-consonant-e, ue

Page 72

Across

1. bread
4. eagle
5. thief
7. elf
8. knead
10. peach
11. tin
12. type
13. wren

Down

1. blind
2. deaf
3. please
5. treat
6. feast
8. kite
9. shy

Page 73

There is one vowel in the middle.
The first vowel has two consonants after it.

1. haste
2. paste
3. kind
4. toll
5. baste
6. cold
7. gold
8. waste
9. bind

wind
Sentences will vary.

MP3418

Answer Key

Page 74

owl, ou   crow, ō   shower, ou   mower, ō
towtruck, ō   growl, ou   rowboat, ō   town, ou
bowl, ō   crown, ou   snowflake, ō   cow, ou

Page 75

flower, clouds, couch, chow, pouch, trout

Page 76

Across
float
smoke
grown
toe
rowboat
vote
globe

Down
lower
throne
know
crow (or grow)
toast
grow (or crow)
stove

Page 77

Across
shout
flower
hour
ground
town

Down
owl
round
house
brown
trout

Page 78

ground, ou   cough, au   tough, u
shawl, au   troll, ō   shout, ou
though, ō   pouch, ou   throw, ō
towel, ou   youth, o͞o   stalk, au
thought, au   gown, ou   soul, ō
plow, ou   growl, ou   lunch, u
cloud, ou   count, ou   flow, ō
sauce, au   shook, o͝o   would, o͝o
grown, ō   bowl, ō   mouse, ou
ought, au   dough, ō   trouble, u
shoe, o͞o   jaw, au   bought, au
should, o͝o   gold, ō   hood, o͝o
hoof, o͝o   young, u   drum, u
found, ou   tooth, o͞o   rough, u
wool, o͝o   soup, o͞o   boat, ō

Page 79

hunters, into, jungle
found, footprints, to, out
noticed
of, toucan, on, bough
cawed, hunters, thought, was, cawing
but, looked
saw, what, was
cougar, was, looking, down
round, hunters, shoot
but, could, not
do, home, without

o͞o	**o͝o**	**u**
into	footprints	hunters
to	looked	jungle
toucan	looking	of
cougar	could	was
shoot		but
do		what

au	**ou**	**ō**
stopped	found	noticed
on	out	home
cawed	bough	
thought	down	
cawing	round	
saw	without	
not		

MP3418

Answer Key

Page 80

1. rescued, wounded
2. soup, coupons
3. used, glue, screw, to
4. crew, continued
5. loon, flew, blue
6. goose, stew
7. baboon, cougar, zoo
8. truth, who, threw, through
9. rooster, cooed
10. stew, chew
11. group, booth
12. knew, cue, to
13. blew, blue
14. screwdrivers, tools
15. few, tulips, bloomed
16. blue, pool
17. due, two
18. group's, clue, loose
19. new, stool, to, school
20. goose. grew, too, to, stew
21. you, renew, overdue
22. moon, threw, onto

ou, u, oo, o, ew, ue

Page 81

$\overline{oo}$

Across	Down
choose	cougar
truth	smooth
view	two
toucan	cue
crew	
hue	

$\bar{o}$

Across	Down
sew	soul
gold	float
though	throw
blow	home
most	

MP3418

FIRESIDE

I Paint

A Fireside Book
Published by Simon and Schuster
New York